THE EYE-BRAIN CONNECTION

eyeQ

Results in Just 7 Minutes

INFINITE MIND®

Brain Enhancement Technology

THE EYE BRAIN CONNECTION
PAGE TURNING TRAINING

Overview

Before computers became common in schools, the methods in this booklet were used in Japan for eye training and brain stimulation. Research has proven that when you include page turning training with the AcceleREAD software program, advanced levels of speed reading can be achieved.

There are three primary purposes for page turning training:
1) As your reading speed increases, you'll need to turn pages faster and smoother with minimal interruption to your focus.
2) As the pages touch your thumb, the stimulation activates your right brain, enhancing the learning process.
3) Fanning every book prior to reading reestablishes your rapid reading pace.

Instructions

Practice cupping your fingers as if holding a briefcase. (see booklet cover) Set your book in your cupped hand with the thumb extended to stabilize the cover. Your opposite hand will hold the entire set of pages in a steady position. Rotate the hand holding the book and allow each page to slowly release from your stable thumb. Practice fanning the entire book 30 times, once each second. Then, fan the entire book over a 4- second period, repeating 7 times. Next, try fanning the entire book over an 8-second period, repeating 4 times. Next, fan the entire book over a 16-second period, repeating 2 times. Finally, fan the book once over a 30-second period. Practice fanning the pages as smoothly as possible.

As you learn to fan the pages evenly (without clumping) you will develop an even, steady reading pattern. Keep this booklet in your briefcase, car or at home so you can practice when you don't have your computer with you. As you practice, you will soon realize how much material the brain can scan in a short period. This exercise will help condition the brain to parallel-process (or scan) information without reading individual words.

EYE EXERCISE & READING INSTRUCTIONS

Left Hand Page-Turning Training

Hold the book in your left hand. Now fan the book with your right thumb slowly releasing each page as you rotate your left wrist. Scan the left pages only.
Left hand training begins on page 2 and ends on page 240. Fan the pages at a speed that is comfortable for you. Practice 3 to 4 exercises per session.

Exercise One	**Circles and Squares - Black/Blue** Watch each object in the center of the pages expand and contract. First circles then squares.
Exercise Three	**Small Squares** Follow the solid squares on the left edge of the pages as they move up and down.
Exercise Four	**Flow Reading (1-2 words)** Focus on the words as they flow across the top of the pages beginning with "The Swiss" on page 2.
Exercise Five	**Small Running Animals** Follow the animals as they alternate top and bottom on every other page, move as quickly as your eyes can follow.
Exercise Six	**Multiple Word Reading** Focus on the blue sentence at the top of each page beginning with "Dorothy lived. . . " on page 2. As you fan the book, see how many words you can recognize at a glance without reading each word separately.

Right Hand Page-Turning Training

Hold the book in your right hand. Now fan the book (back to front) with your left thumb slowly releasing each page as you rotate your right wrist. Scan the right pages only. Right hand training begins on page 239 and ends on page 1.

Exercise Two	**Flow Reading (1-2 words)** Focus on the black words as they flow across the center of the page beginning with "Many" on page 239 and ending on page 1.
Exercise Seven	**Block Reading (multiple lines)** Follow the blue words as they flow across the top of the page begining with "you" on page 239. Focus on as many of the words as you can and as your field of vision increases, try visualizing the entire paragraph.
Exercise Eight	**Word/Picture Flash** Notice the pictures and corresponding words in the boxes on alternating pages. See how many words & objects you can recognize at a glance. This exercise helps expand your peripheral vision, and teaches you to read *visually* instead of *vocally*.

The eye training exercises in this program have been designed to strengthen the eye muscles. If you experience discomfort or pain during training, stop and rest your eyes. If discomfort or pain persists, discontinue using the program and contact a physician.

The stories in this book are reprinted with permission from Waldman Publishing Corp., New York, NY.

The proprietary eye exercises and reading methods used in this program were acquired from The New Japan Speed Reading Company (Shin Nihon Sokudoku).

INFINITE MIND®, L.C.
5800 East Big Cottonwood Canyon
Salt Lake City, UT 84121

Telephone: 801-453-1700
Toll Free: 888-INF-MIND (Outside of Salt Lake City, UT)
Fax: 801-453-1711
Internet: www.infmind.com

<u>Note: This the last page of Right Hand Turning Exercise</u>

even want to get up to cook breakfast. So I started dozing of again, when suddenly I heard a deep booming sound.

reassured

PITCHER CROWN

Dorothy lived with her Aunt Em and

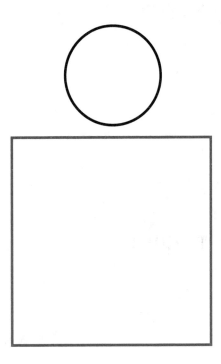

I felt rested and satisfied. A couple of squirrels sat on a limb and jabbered at me in a friendly way. I was lazy and comfortable and didn't

tears and

town of

Uncle Henry on a small farm in Kansas.

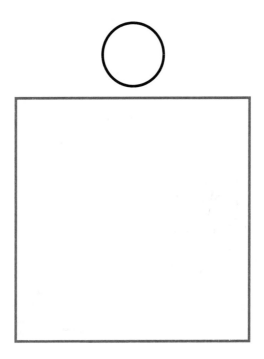

it was after eight o'clock. I lay there on the grass in the cool shade, looking up at the sun through the holes in the branches.

away her

CLIP BOARD

MICROSCOPE

SCALE

Mayenfeld

Their tiny house stood alone on a large,

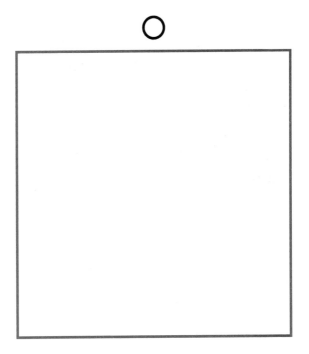

so I stepped into the woods and laid down for a nap before breakfast. The sun was so high in the sky when I woke up that I figured

wiped

lies at the

flat prairie. Dorothy had only one friend,

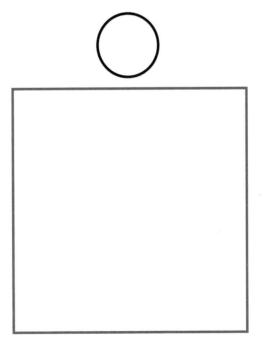

I could almost see the Widow Douglas
inside the big house on the hill. There was
a little gray in the sky now as dawn came on,

Elizabeth,

TRACTOR

SUN

FLAG   ROSE

foot of a

her dog Toto. He was a small black

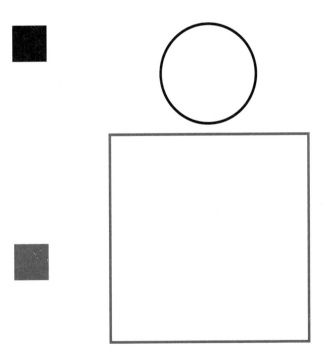

the head of the island. From there, I could
see way over to town, three miles away. The
lights were twinkling, and if I closed my eyes,

My wife,

mountain

dog who loved to jump and play.

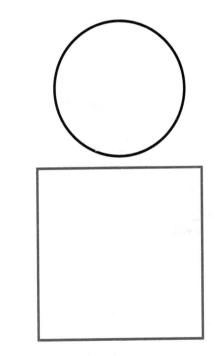

and soon I was on my way. It didn't take
long to get to the island. Once I landed and
tied up my canoe, I headed for the big log at

to him."

AMBULANCE

FLOWER POT

SAIL BOAT

LEAF

AIRPLANE

range

One day while Dorothy and Toto

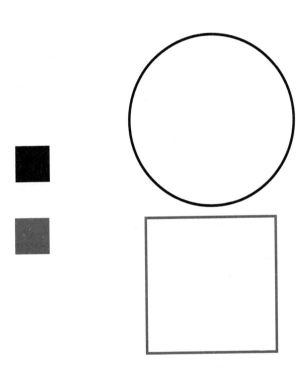

place to hide. So I decided to head for
Jackson's Island. I knew the place pretty well.
When the moon rose, I pushed off in the canoe,

is impossible

whose

were playing, they heard the awful

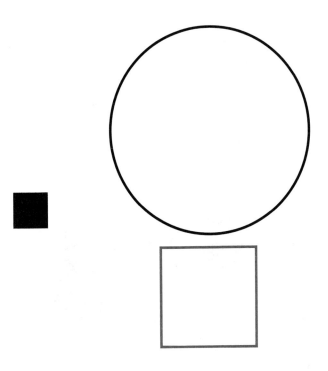

but they would soon get tired of that. Maybe they would hunt for the robbers who broke into the cabin. But right now, I needed to find some

for nothing

CLOUD

NEEDLE   KEYS

SNOW FLAKES

FOOT PRINT   BOTTLE

rugged

sound of a storm. The wind roared

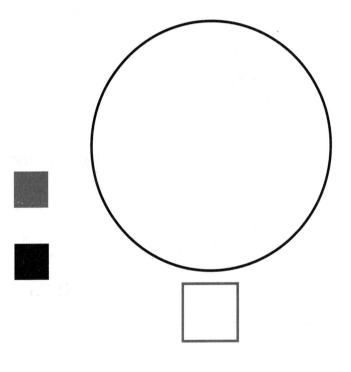

and by laid down in the canoe to smoke my pipe and figure out a plan. I knew the townspeople would drag the river for my body,

save us,

peaks

and the dust blew smoky circles in the air.

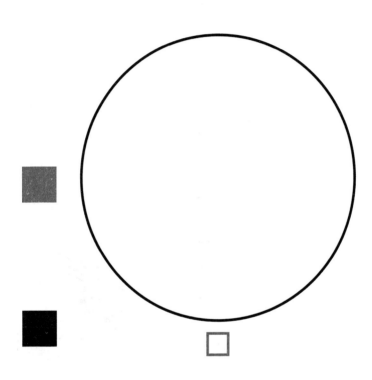

When it was dark, I moved the canoe down the river and waited under some willows for the moon to rise. I took a bite to eat and by

"God will

WAGON

KITE

BLOCKS

BINOCULARS

POCKET KNIFE

BOWLING PIN

DRUM

Dorothy was frightened. Uncle Henry

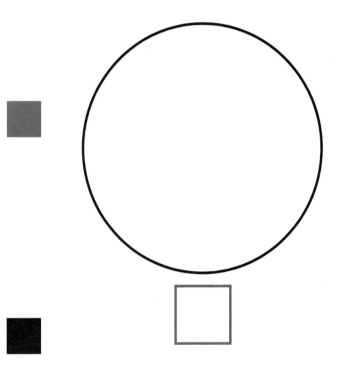

The whole thing looked like someone had hacked his way into the cabin, killed me, and dragged my body off somewhere.

me trembling.

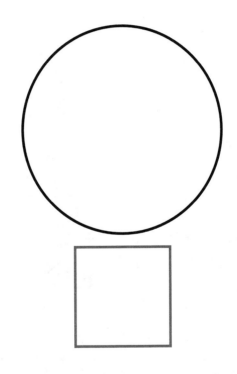

above the

stopped working and shouted,

and let it's blood make a trail wherever I
dragged it. Then I pulled out some of my hair
and stuck it and the axe on the cabin door.

clung to

BIKE   KNIFE

BASKETBALL

DOLL

BUS

APPLE

TENNIS RACKET

BASEBALL

valley

"There's a cyclone coming,

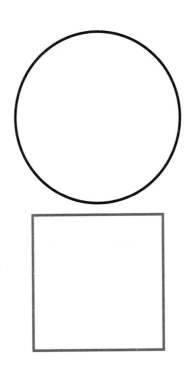

and shot a pig. I found Pap's axe and used it to smash the cabin door to bits. Next, I fetched the pig inside, cut open its throat,

who

below.

run for the cellar!" A cyclone is a

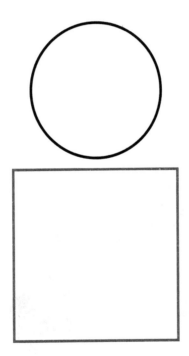

to the cabin and covered up the hole I had made. As part of my plan, I took Pap's shotgun from its hiding place, then went into the woods

Francis, 8,

MOON

SOCCERBALL   HELMET

IN-LINE SKATE

BAT

WHISTLE

GOLF CART

RIFLE

FOOTBALL

Behind the

terrible storm. Even little Toto wanted

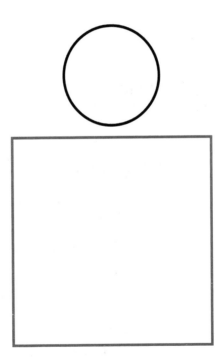

and coffee, and headed down to the river. I
filled the canoe with string, matches, a tin
cup, and some blankets. Then I went back

and

to run away.   He jumped from

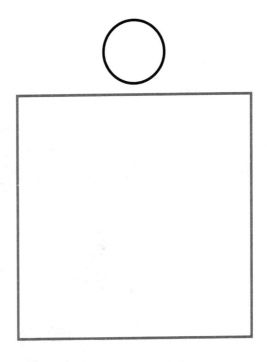

and I was out. I knew where there was an old canoe tied up on the shore, so I took a sack of cornmeal, a side of bacon, some sugar,

Ernest, 11,

GOLF CLUBS   HAT   TIE

WATCH   WAGON

SUN GLASSES

CANDLE

RING   HEART

STAR   BOOT

winds gently

Dorothy's arms, ran into the house,

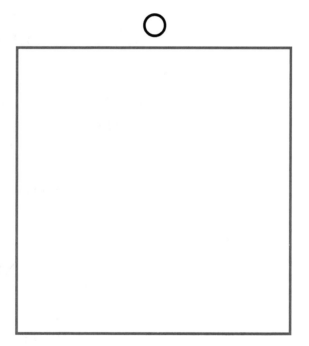

so I waited until he had a good start, then I
pulled out my saw. Before he was on the
other side of the river, the hole was finished,

Jack, 13,

up the

and hid under the bed.   Dorothy followed

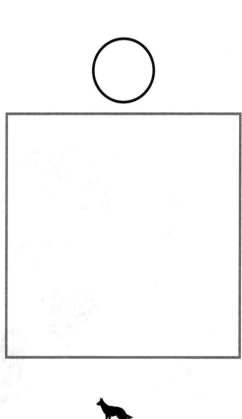

really be free. After we had dinner, Pap locked me up in the cabin and went back to town. I judged he wouldn't come back that night,

Fritz, 15,

BOW

JUG

CAKE

BALLOONS

GIFT

CUP AND
SAUCER

BREAD   EGGS

GRILL

STRAWBERRY

ICE CREAM CONE

CORN

mountain.

him into the house. Then a strange

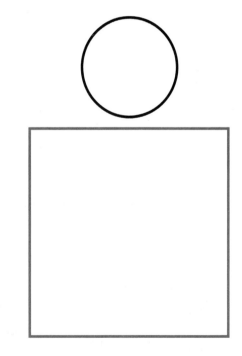

place where no one would find me. So I
decided that if I could keep Pap and the
Widow from trying to find me then I would

sons,

One sunny

thing happened. The house turned

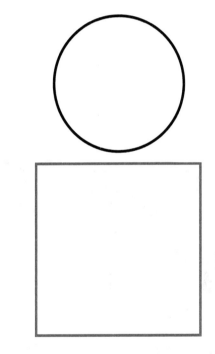

She had sent a man to try to follow Pap, but Pap drove him off with his shotgun. After that, he threatened to hide me in another

my four

LOBSTER

PIE

CARROT

APPLE

GLOBE

PEN

MILK

CAKE

DAY PLANNER   STAMP   TACK

June morning,

around and around. Then it rose

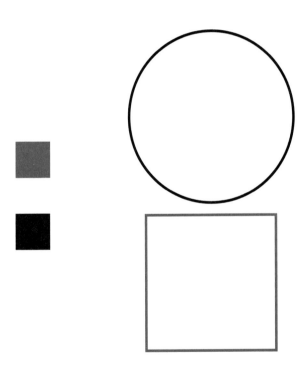

a long time, and there would be no money until the court made a decision. Meanwhile, the Widow had been looking for me.

I said to

a tall,

through the air! Toto ran out from

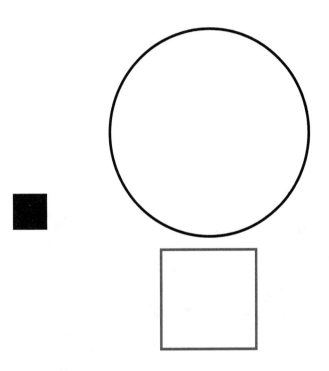

usual mood---a bad one. He said he had been downtown, and everything was going wrong. His lawyer said the trial would take

be afraid."

BRIEFCASE   SCISSORS

PENCIL

STAPLER   HOUSE

TEPEES

BARN

CHURCH

HANGERS   BOOTS

under the bed and barked loudly.

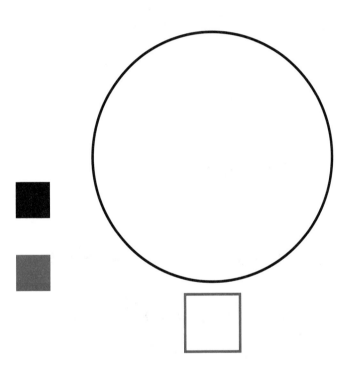

the woods. I got rid of the signs of my work dropped the blanket over the hole, and hid my saw. Pretty soon Pap came in. He was in his

musn't

It was very dark and the house

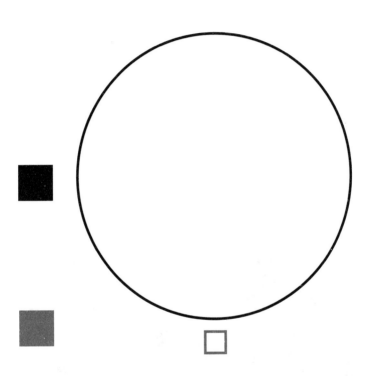

big bottom log for me to escape through. Well, it was a long job, but I was getting towards the end when I heard Pap's gun in

"You

BOOKS	CANDY CANE	
WINDMILL		BELL
	CLOWN	
WAGON		
	SAXOPHONE	PALETTE
CANNON		

climbing up

swayed back and forth. Dorothy held

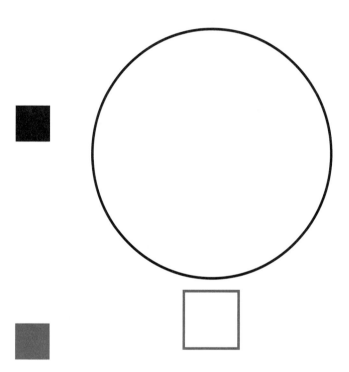

was an old horse blanket nailed against the log wall. I got under the table, raised the blanket, and went to work sawing out a section of the

prayer.

the path.

Toto in her arms and listened to the wind.

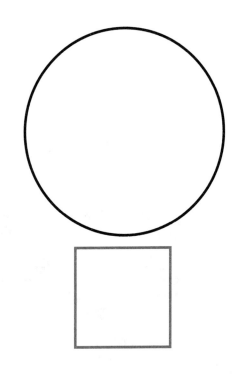

a broken handle. I fixed the handle and looked for a place to start sawing. There, behind a table at the far end of the cabin,

knees in

BALLERINA

PIANO

MICROPHONE

FILM

TOP HAT

FISH

DRUM

PENGUIN

She had a

She was frightened. Aunt Em and

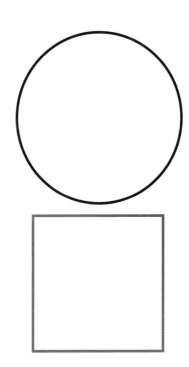

the chimney was too narrow to climb up,
and the door was made of thick solid oak
slabs. Finally I found an old rusty saw with

their

bundle in

Uncle Henry were safe in the cellar.

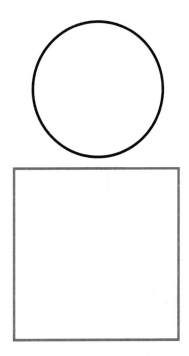

not to leave a knife or anything in the cabin for me to cut through the floor. The windows weren't big enough for even a dog to get through,

fell to

TURKEY

VIOLIN

SPIDER

SEA HORSE

ROOSTER   PIG   DOG

one hand

She was all alone. Hours passed.

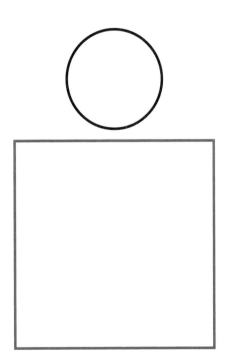

I had tried to get out of that cabin many a times, but I just couldn't figure out how. When Pap was away, he was pretty careful

sailors

and held a

The house tossed and turned in the storm.

and scared. I thought maybe he had drowned, and I was sure I would never get out again. I had to figure out some way to escape.

the frightened

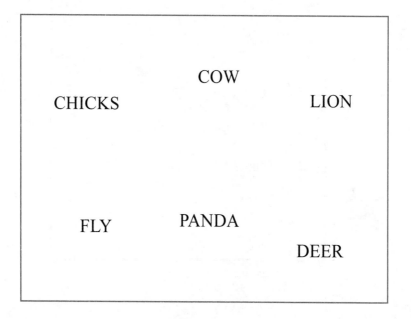

COW

CHICKS

LION

FLY

PANDA

DEER

little girl

Finally Dorothy closed her eyes and

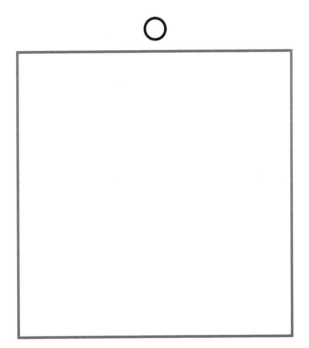

and he would lock me in the cabin so I couldn't escape. Once, he locked me in and was gone for three days. I was terribly lonesome

course,

fell asleep. After a long time,

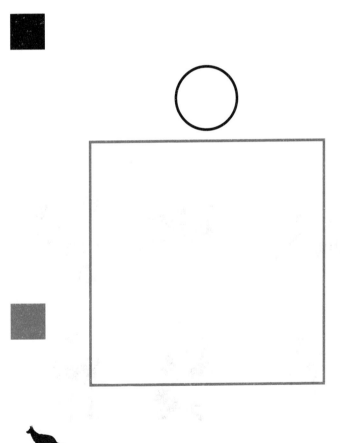

Pap got too handy with his belt when he got drunk, and I couldn't stand it. I was covered with welts. He got to going away a lot too,

us far off

GUITAR   DUCK

STARFISH

OWL   CHICKEN

years old

Dorothy woke up. Everything was

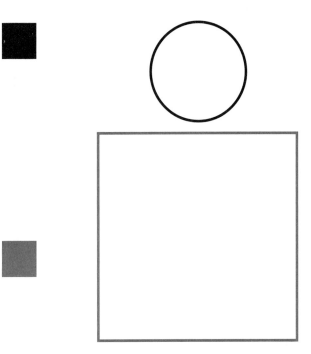

He'd fetch it home and get drunk. Then he'd lock the door at night and put the key under his head alongside his gun. But by and by,

had driven

by the

very quiet. Bright sunshine came

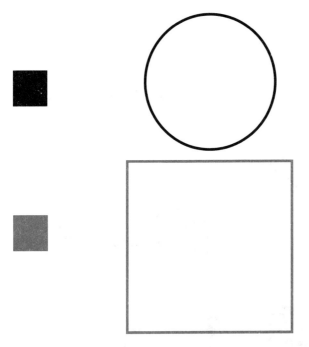

food we hunted and fished. Every once in a while Pap locked me in the cabin and went to the store to trade fish and game for whiskey.

storm

KANGAROO

KITTEN

MOUSE

ELEPHANT

other hand.

through the windows. Toto pressed

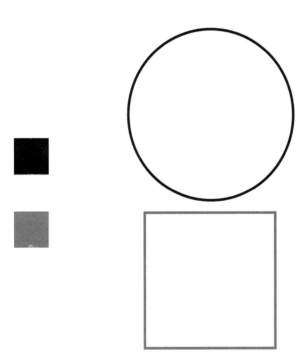

We walked through the woods until we
came to the old log cabin where we once
lived. For the next few months, we lived on the

that the

his cold nose against Dorothy's face.

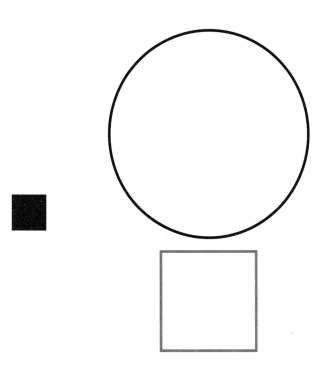

up the river about three miles and crossed
over to the Illinois shore where it was
woody and deserted with no houses.

Realizing

COINS

CLOCK

RABBIT

cheeks

"Where am I?" asked Dorothy.

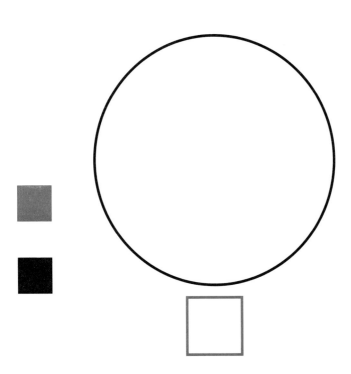

make trouble for him. This got the old man real angry. So he watched for me, and one day in the spring he grabbed me. He took me

water.

were

"What happened to Uncle Henry

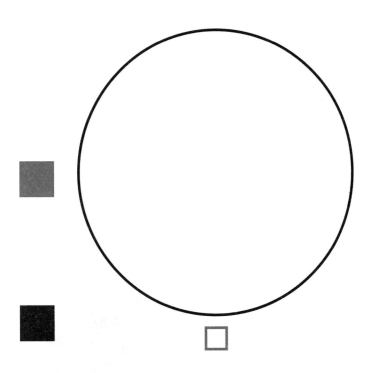

This happened again and again. He got to hanging around the Widow's so much that she told him if he didn't quit it, she would

fill with

FILE CABINET

RATTLESNAKE

flushed and

and Aunt Em? She ran to the door

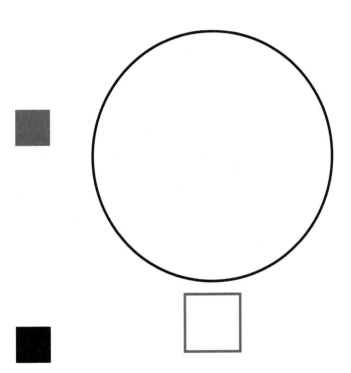

judge to give to Pap. Whenever he got the
money, he got drunk and made a big
commotion in town. Then he was thrown in jail.

begin to

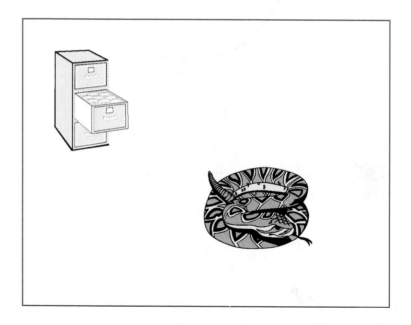

sunburned,

and looked out at a magical land.

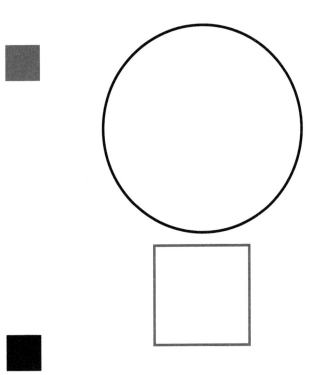

When the judge refused, Pap went to court. The trial went slowly, so every now and then I had to borrow some money from the

ship

COMPASS

GIRAFFE

PAPER CLIP

and she

All around her were beautiful green

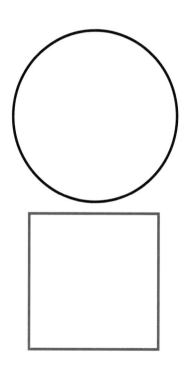

and he went to see Judge Thatcher. He shouted and threatened that he'd get the law on the judge if he didn't give him the money.

and the

was wearing

trees and colorful flowers. Tiny purple

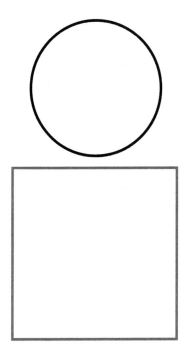

and he took the dollar the judge had given me. I knew he'd go downtown to buy some whiskey. The next day he was drunk,

appeared,

BUNNY

CLOCK

CALCULATOR

MAIL BOX

two dresses,

birds sang as they flew from tree to tree.

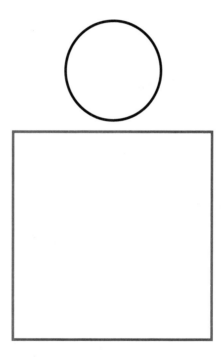

he said angrily, "and find out where the money is and get my hands on it one way or the other." Then he made me empty my pockets,

leaks

Dorothy had never seen such a lovely place.

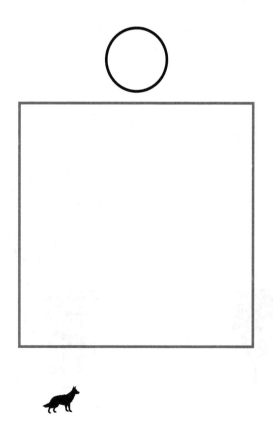

"But no mind, where's the money?" I told him that I gave it all to Judge Thatcher, but he didn't believe me. "I'll go see the judge,"

Several

BUTTERFLY   ANT

BAT   SANDWICH   PIZZA

of the other.

Suddenly she heard a small voice say,

me to learn how to read and write and dress and live like a civilized human being. "It's that widow out to steal my own son," he cried.

the sea.

She looked

"Welcome to the Land of the Munchkins."

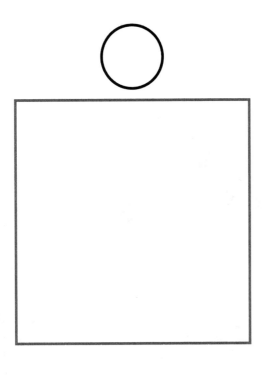

don't you? Who told you you could meddle with such foolishness, huh? Who told you?"
I explained to Pap that the Widow wanted

fell into

IRON

WITCH

JACK-O-LANTERN

PIANO

TELEVISION

MIXER

like a

Dorothy turned around and there

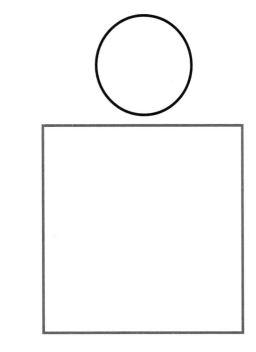

before I'm done with you. I hear you can read and write now too. I bet you think you're better than your own father now,

apart and

were three men and one woman

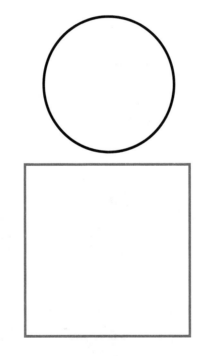

I answered. "Don't you give me any of your lip," he snorted. "You've put on airs since I've been away. I'll take you down a peg or two

ripped

```
TOASTER                    CAMERA

          WREATH
                    LIGHT BULB



     FIREPLACE
              CHAIR        SNOWMAN
```

bundle of

standing in a circle. They were all

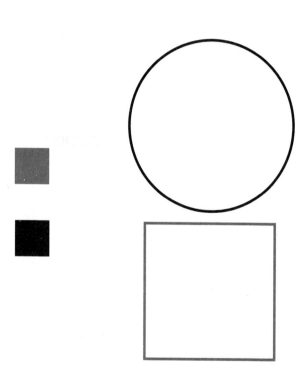

"Fancy clothes you got there," he said.
"You think you're a big shot now, don't
you?" "Maybe I am and maybe I'm not,"

masts

clothing

the same size as Dorothy, but they

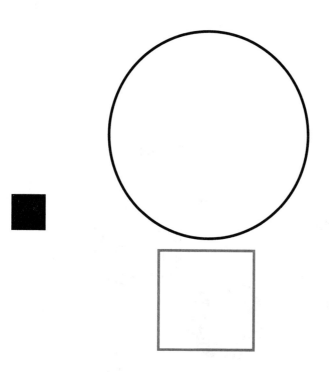

black slouch hat with the top caved in was laying on the floor near his feet. We stared at each other, then Pap looked me up and down.

the

BED

ALARM
CLOCK

LADDER

LAMP

ROCKING
CHAIR

WINDOW

FLASH LIGHT

RADIO

trudging

looked like grown-ups. They wore

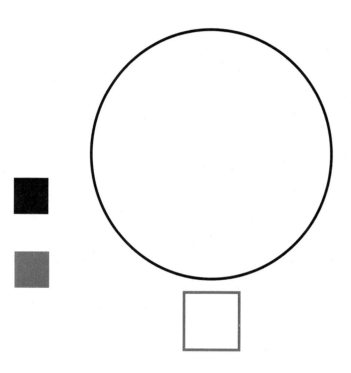

other knee. The boot on his raised foot was busted, and two of his toes stuck through. His clothes were all in rags, and his old

day,

hats that rose to small point about a

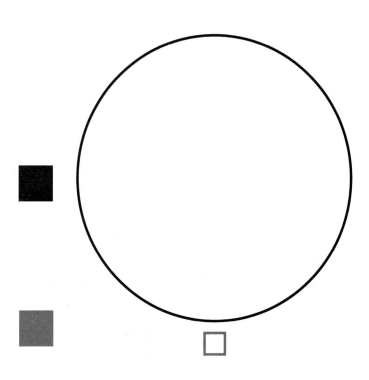

that could make a person sick, a white to make a person's flesh crawl. He was sitting on my bed with one ankle resting on the

seventh

HAMMER   COMB

UMBRELLA

FIRE   KNIFE
EXTINGUISHER

FEATHER

SCREW

MOWER   SAW HORSE

pair of

foot above their heads. Tiny bells

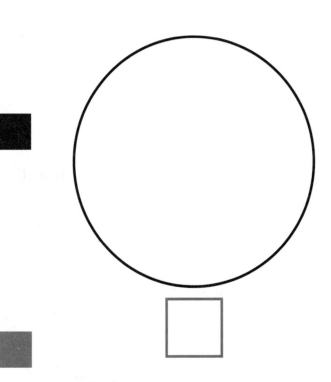

through like he was behind vines. There wasn't any color in his face. It was white, but not like another man's white. It was a white

On the

shoes. After

tinkled when they moved. The men

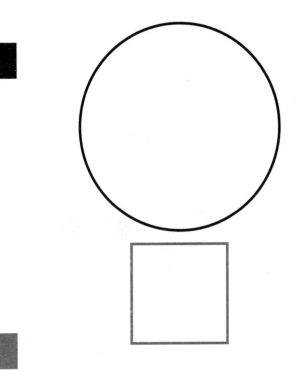

and black, no gray. But it was tangled and greasy and hung down into his long, mixed-up whiskers. You could see his eyes shining

the air.

| BASKET | | WHEEL |
| | SUN DIAL | BARROW |

TROWEL

PAINT
BRUSH   TEA POT

FORK

LADLE

HAIR DRYER
ROLLING PIN

climbing for

wore strange blue suits and had long

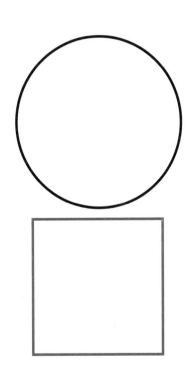

a good look at the old man, and he didn't
look that frightening at all. He was almost
fifty, and he looked it. His hair was long

high in

white beards. The woman wore a

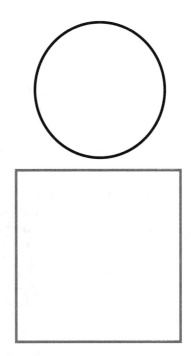

there he was! Pap. I used to be scared of
him all the time because he hit me so much
when he was drunk and all. But now I took

tossing it

CURLING
IRON
      WAFFLE
      IRON
TRICERATOPS

      DONKEY
ROOSTER

LAMB
      BUTTERFLY
STEGOSAURUS

GOAT   TOUCAN   TURKEY

hour, they

long gown covered with stars.

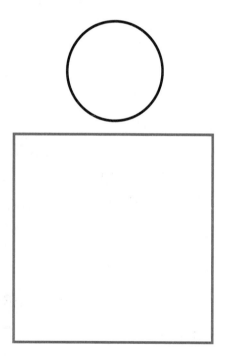

Once inside, I lit my candle and went up to my room. I shut the door and breathed a big sigh of relief. But then I turned around...

ship,

reached a

She made a bow, and in a sweet

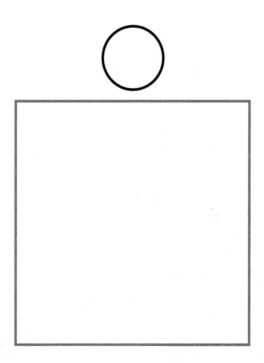

what I said. He asked me to sign a paper to make it all legal. I did it and left. I hurried back to the Widow's. At least there, I'd be safe.

wooden

TYRANNOSAURUS
REX   COW

                BULL

                           PIGLET
            PIG
HORSE

        ROAD
        RUNNER
                    SCORPION
SEA GULL
                            SPIDER
        DOG
        HOUSE   PEGASUS

voice said, "How can we thank you

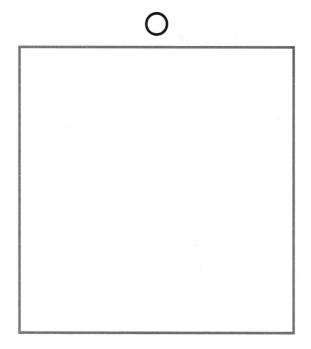

"Please don't ask me any more questions, sir. I know what I'm doing all right." After a while, I convinced the Judge that I meant

our little

called

for killing the Wicked Witch of the East?

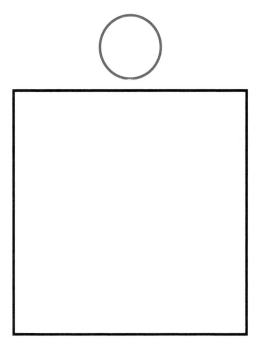

want me to take it Huck? What can you mean
by giving away all your money like this?

against

DOG
HOUSE
LAMB
PELICAN
GRASSHOPPER

COBRA
UNICORN
POODLE
PUPPY

COLLIE
BULL FROG
DOG BONE

Dorfli. This

You have set us free!" Dorothy was shocked.

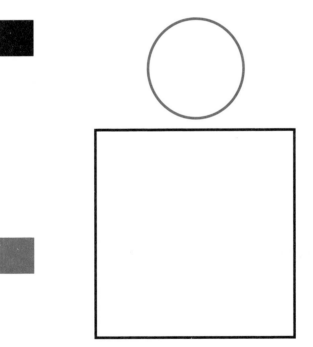

thousand too!" The Judge looked surprised. He couldn't figure me out. "Why do you

pounded

was where

"There must be some mistake,"

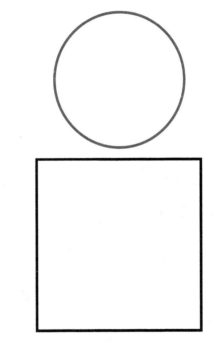

breathlessly. "I don't want you to invest it.
I want you to take it---the interest and the six

waves

BEAR   ARMADILLO

BAT

ALLIGATOR

BALL OF
YARN

GERMAN
SHEPHERD   SNAIL

TURTLE

SCOTTISH
CAT   TERRIER

the woman

she said, "I have not killed

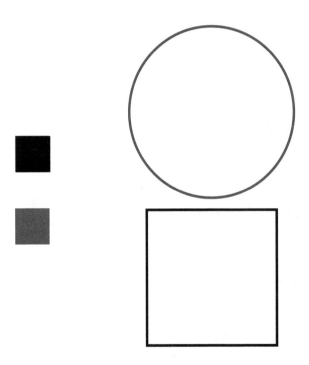

page 126

You had better let me invest it for you along with your six thousand." "No, sir," I explained

while the

used to

anyone." The tiny woman pointed to

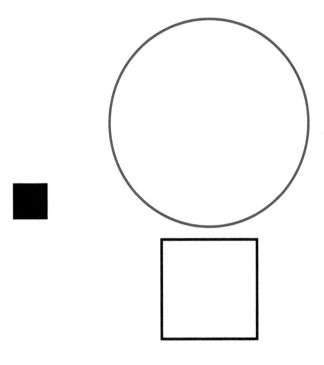

half-yearly check came in last night---over a hundred fifty dollars. Quite a fortune for you.

sails,

ANGEL
FISH

AQUARIUM

BUMBLE
BEE

FOX

POLAR
BEAR

DRAGON
FLY

ELEPHANT

COYOTE

PANDA
BEAR

live, and the

the house. "Look, your house landed on

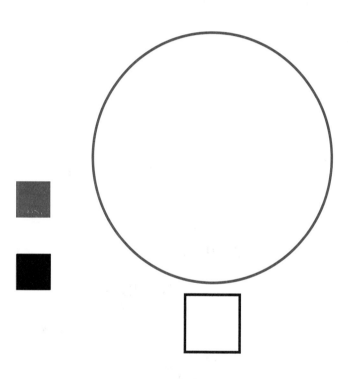

"Did you come for your interest?" "No, sir,"
I answered "Is there some?" "Oh yes, a

at the

people of

the Witch. Those are her feet sticking

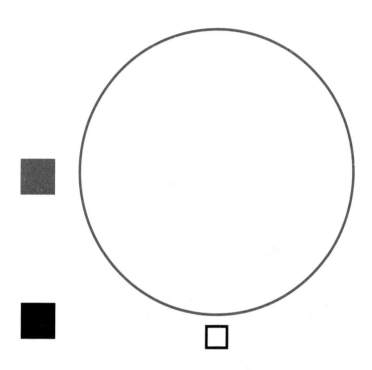

few minutes. "Why Huck, you're all out of breath," he said as he opened the door.

and tore

KOALA BEAR   BEAVER   BISON

SQUIRREL   FAWN

WARTHOG   CHIPMUNK   CAMEL

the town

out from under a block of wood."

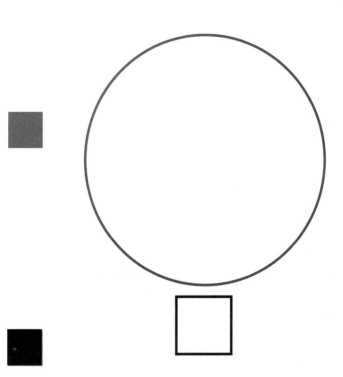

every few seconds, but I didn't see anyone.
I reached Judge Thatcher's house in a

howled

"Oh dear!" cried Dorothy.

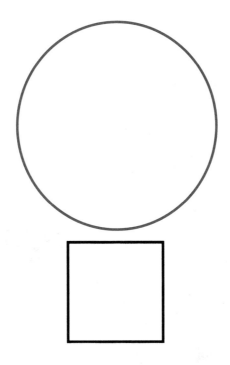

and running down the hill as fast as my legs
could carry me. I looked over my shoulder

the wind

MOOSE		KANGAROO
	PORCUPINE	
CHIMPANZEE		
	RHINOCEROS	
HIPPOPOTAMUS		GIRAFFE

bered her

"I'm so sorry." "There is nothing

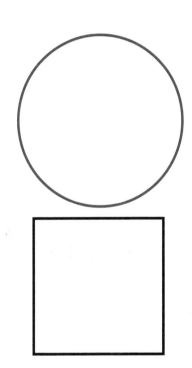

into the heel---a good luck sign. I had seen
the heel print before...! Suddenly, I was up

day,

and called

you can do," said the woman. "She

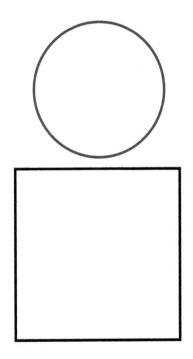

boot heel was in the shape of a cross. It was
formed by two big nails imbedded crossways

seventh

MOUSE CASTLE RACCOON

SKUNK LION TIGER

to her from

was a very wicked Witch, and she

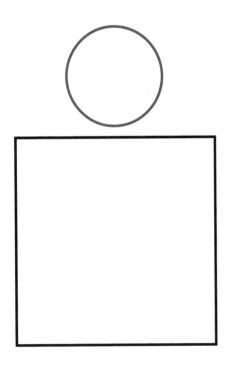

tracks when something stopped me. The impression made in the snow by the left

On the

their houses.

made the Munchkins slaves for

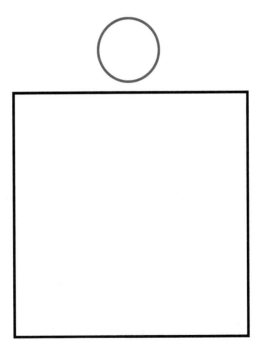

around. I couldn't figure it out. It was very strange somehow. I was about to follow the

the air.

```
┌─────────────────────────────────────┐
│                                       │
│   BUILDINGS                           │
│                              HOUSE    │
│              IGLOO                     │
│                                       │
│                                       │
│                           LEANING     │
│                           TOWER       │
│       WINDMILL            OF PISA     │
│                                       │
└─────────────────────────────────────┘
```

es. She did

many years. Now thanks to you,

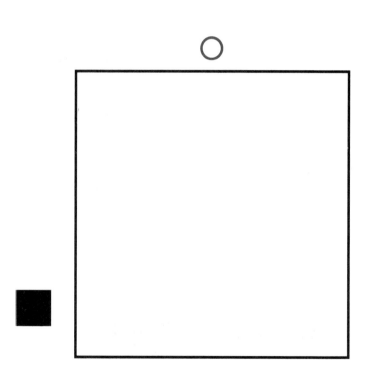

then went on around the garden. It was
funny he hadn't come in, after standing

high in

not answer,

we are free!" "Are you a Munchkin?"

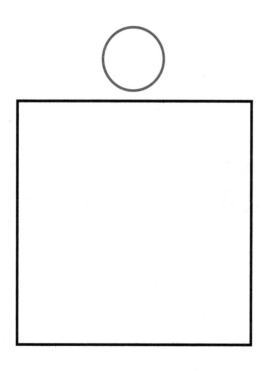

Whoever made them had come up from the quarry and stood around the fence for a while,

tossing it

ARTIST

WATER
COLORS

CRAYONS

BARBERS
POLE

but continued

asked Dorothy, "no," answered the woman

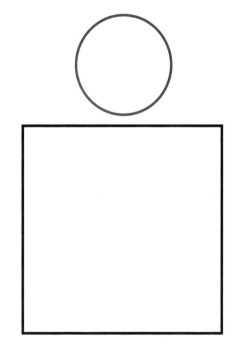

inch of new snow on the ground, and I
stopped when I saw some fresh tracks.

ship,

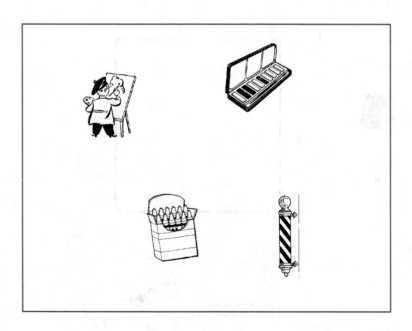

ued on her

. "I am the Good Witch of the North."

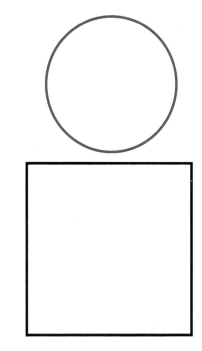

I went down to the front yard and climbed over the high board fence. There was an

wooden

BARBER

ZEBRA

COLOSEUM

way until

Dorothy had never heard of a good witch.

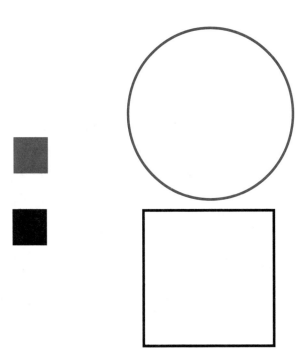

happened to drop the salt shaker at breakfast. This was sure to be my bad luck day.

our little

she

But the kind woman explained that

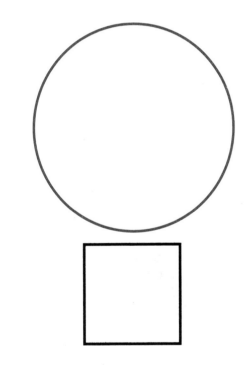

I slept outside whenever I could slip away. It made the house easier to take. One morning I

against

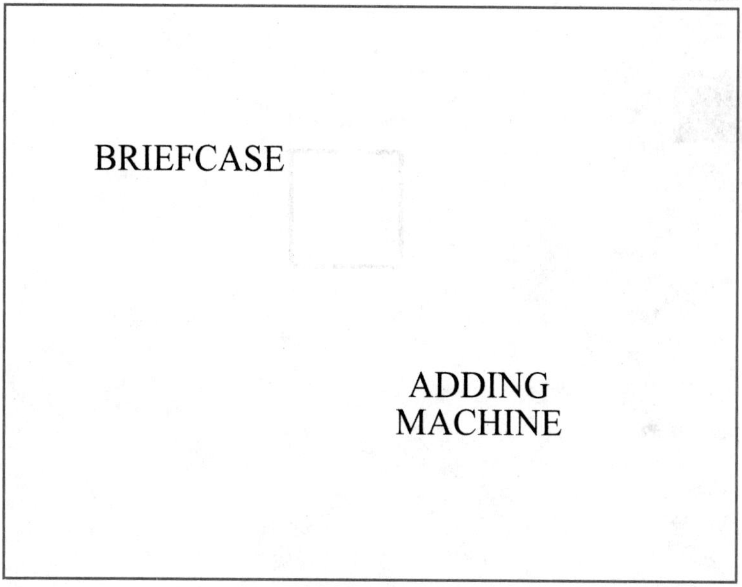

BRIEFCASE

ADDING
MACHINE

reached a

Dorothy was now in the Land of Oz.

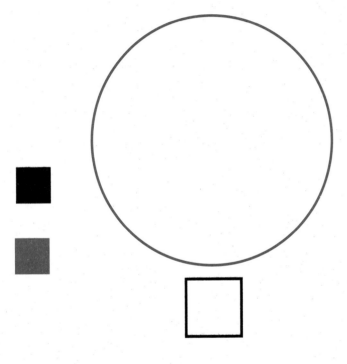

sleeping in a bed made me feel a little too
civilized. So, before the cold weather came on,

pounded

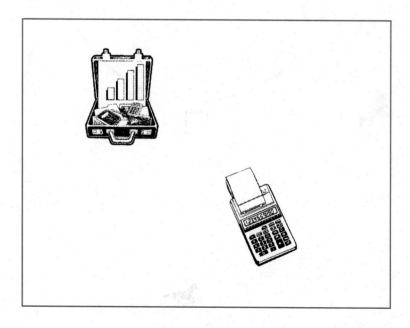

In the Land of Oz there were four witches.

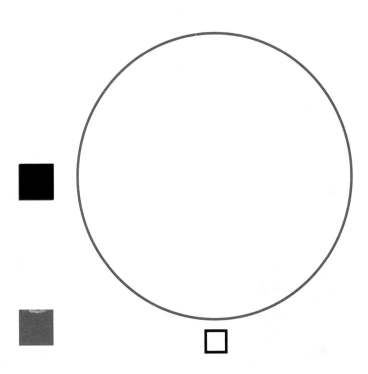

the easier it got. I sort of got used to the
Widow's ways, but living in a house and

waves

PRINTER

FAX MACHINE

TELEPHONE

the very

The witches who lived in the North

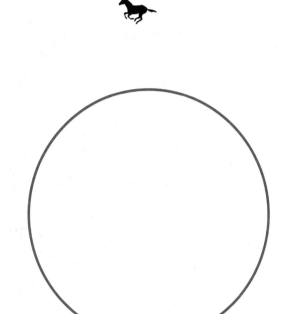

and write and do a little arithmetic. At
first I hated school, but the more I went,

while the

end of the

and South were good witches,

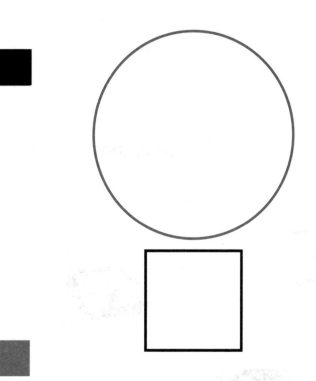

all started school again.   It was the first time
for me, but I could already spell and read

sails,

SCANNER   DOLLAR
                                      SIGN

        DUMP   PENNY
        TRUCK

main street.

and the people loved them. But the witches

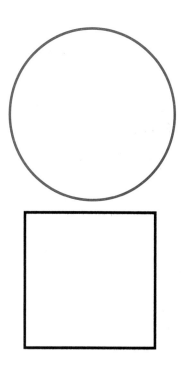

for a little while. After three or four months had passed, our little club broke up, and we

at the

There a

who lived in the East and West were wicked.

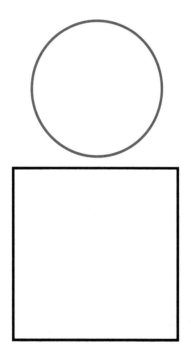

the grease and clay and looked so sorry that
I thought I would behave if I could, at least

and tore

PIGGY BANK

COMPUTER

OIL CAN

DRAFTING
TABLE
LAMP

voice from

"Now you have killed the Wicked

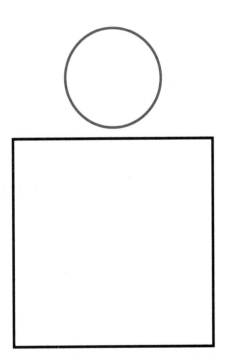

Miss Watson because of my clothes, but the Widow didn't scold me. She just cleaned off

howled

inside

Witch of the East," explained the

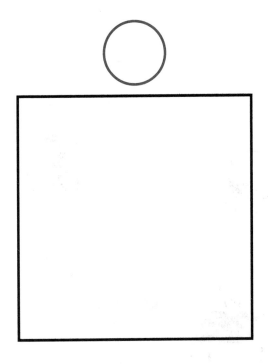

of clay, and I was dog-tired. Well, I got a
good going-over in the morning from old

the wind

		LAP TOP
		COMPUTER
CALCULATOR		
	CD	
		KEY
DISKETTE		
	NICKEL	

called to her:

gentle woman." There is only one

page 174

crept into my window just before daybreak.
My new clothes were greased-up and full

days,

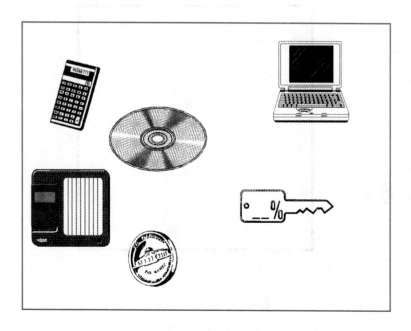

"Half a

Wicked Witch still alive."

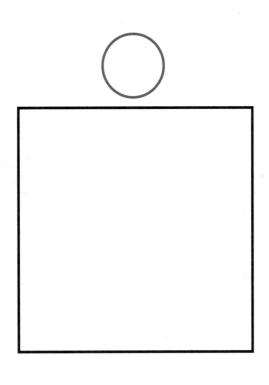

and Joe Harper second captain, and then we started home. I climbed up the shed and

For six

POT OF
GOLD   PAPER CLIP

COMBINATION
LOCK

FACTORY

MAGNIFYING
GLASS

OIL DERRICK

STAPLER

minute,

Now Dorothy understood. She was happy

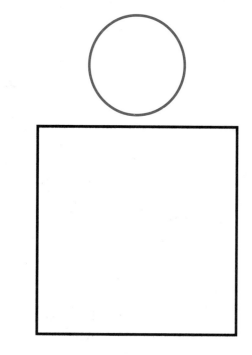

a little while, and then we all took an oath
of loyalty to the club. We elected Tom captain

storm.

Detie,

to have helped the Munchkins,

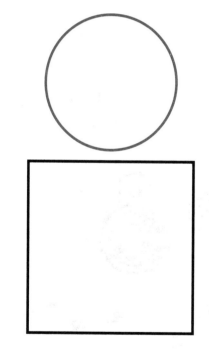

There was me and Tom and Ben Rogers and Tommy Barnes and Joe Harper. We talked for

violent

BACK HOE

STAMP

RUBBER STAMP

TACK

SUN GLASSES

BELL

PRESENT

BALLOONS

and I'll

but she wanted to return to Kansas

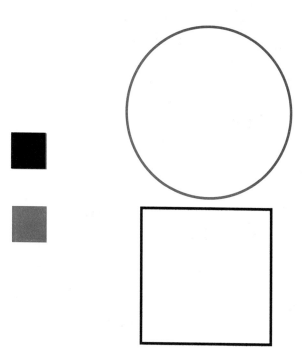

window in a flash. We all met by a clump
of bushes not far from the Widow's house.

ran into a

and see her Uncle Henry and Aunt Em.

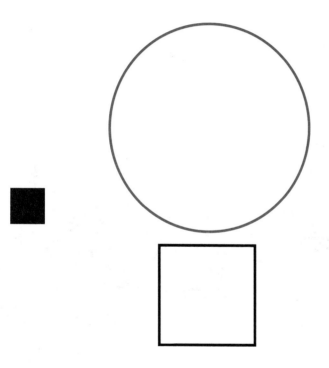

with my own "Meow." Then I slipped into my clothes very quietly and was out the

way we

BASEBALL CAP

SOCKS

BASKETBALL SHOE

COWBOY BOOT

HIGH HEEL SHOE

DAY PACK

UMBRELLA

PURSE

EYE GLASSES

you if

The Good Witch and the Munchkins

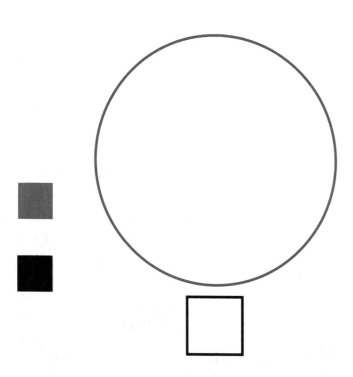

Tom's signal. He had called a midnight
meeting of our club. I answered his signal

Along the

you're

had never even heard of Kansas.

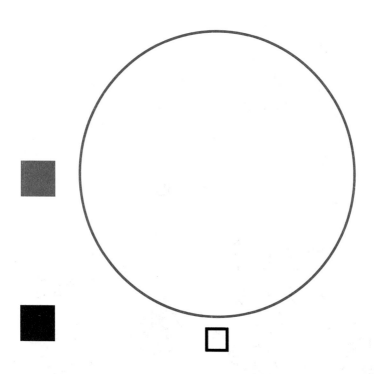

After a while, I heard a "Meow! Meow!
coming from beneath my window. It was

a colony.

DIPLOMA

TEE SHIRT

WATCH

RING

BONNET

GLOVE

MITTENS

BASKET

SEWING
MACHINE

NEEDLE AND
THREAD

going any

Dorothy was a long, long way from home.

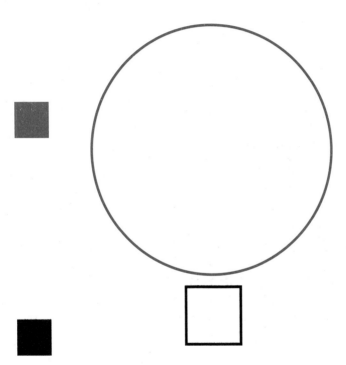

I sat in the quiet house and listened for the sound of the wind or the rustle of the trees.

establish

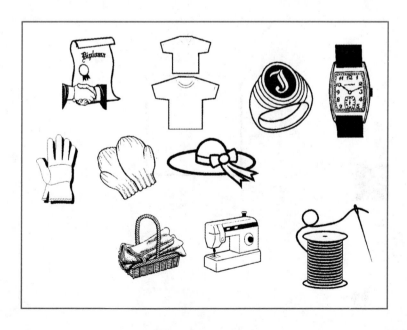

farther."

She began to cry. She felt very lonely

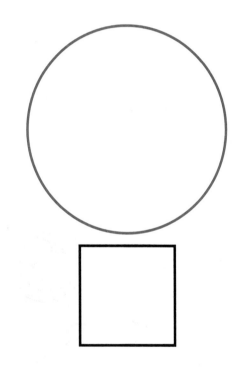

candle for light. One night after my lesson,
I felt so unhappy there, I wished I was dead.

were to

SCISSORS STAPLE
REMOVER STAPLER

MAGNIFYING
GLASS GRADUATE

DOLLY WEDDING
CAKE

SAFETY
PIN BUS

BELL BOOKS

Detie,

in this strange land. When the Good Witch

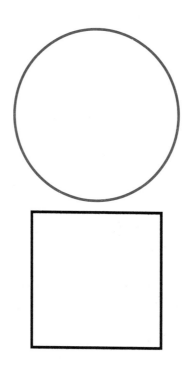

made me tired and lonesome. By and by, she would send me to bed with a piece of

where we

stood still,

saw that Dorothy was crying,

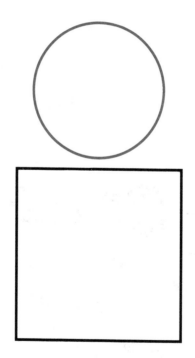

immediate interest in me and tried to teach
me to read and spell. These lessons just

Guinea,

PENCIL

COMPASS   KEY   DESK
                CHAIN

              LUNCH BOX   PENCIL
                                SHARPENER

CRAYONS
              PENCIL AND
              NOTE PAD

CORRECTION
   FLUID   TROPHY
                          SEAL
              NEWSPAPER

but the little

she took off her cap and balanced

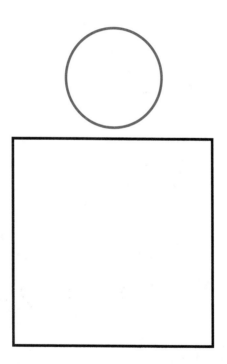

Miss Watson, the Widow's sister, who had just come to live with her. She took an

near New

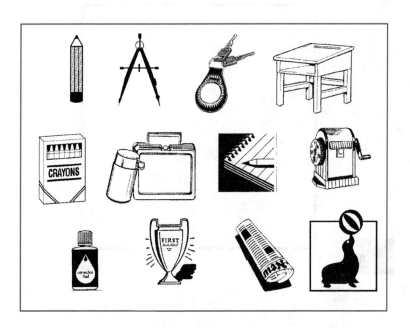

the point on the end of her nose.

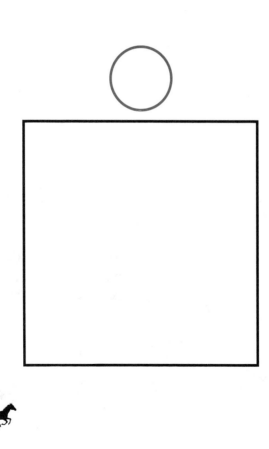

I had the hardest time getting used to regular meals and polite talk. Then there was

island

CIRCUS TENT   CLOWN   JUGGLER   FERRIS WHEEL

BLACK BOARD   ERASER AND CHALK   DANCING

COUNTY FAIR   CAMERA

CAROUSEL   FILM

down on

She counted to three. The cap changed

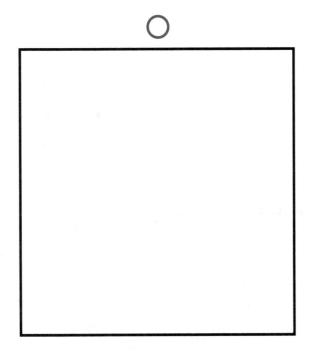

in a new suit of clothes that made me feel uncomfortable and sweaty all over again.

was an

the ground.

into a slate. On the slate were the words,

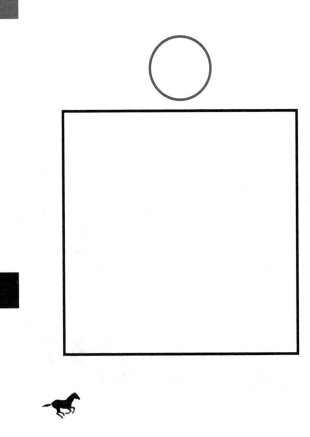

So I went back, and the Widow cried over me, calling me a "poor lost lamb." She put me

destination

BALLET SLIPPERS

ACCORDION

MAESTRO

MUSIC NOTE

DRAMA MASKS

TAMBOURINE

GUITAR

SINGER

VIOLIN AND BOW

TRIANGLE

"Tired,

"Let Dorothy go to the Emerald City."

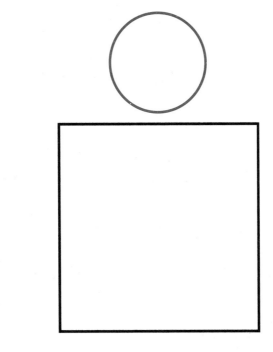

a member if I went back to living a
respectable life with the Widow Douglas.

Our

Heidi?"

Dorothy dried her tears. "You must go

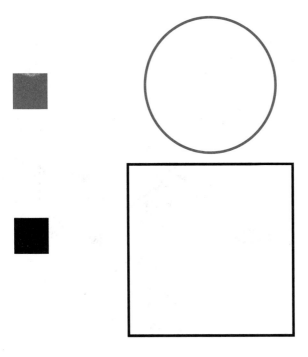

But Tom Sawyer hunted me up and said he
was going to start a club and I could only be

Ocean.

LIGHTS

HAT AND
CANE

MICROPHONE

DRUM

TRUMPET
PLAYER

SAXOPHONE

TUBA
PLAYER

PIANO

LP RECORD

Detie asked

to the Emerald City. Maybe the Wizard

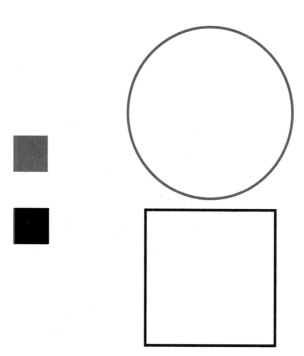

stand it any more, I ran away and got into my old rags. Then I felt free and happy.

Pacific

her.

of Oz can help you," said the Good Witch.

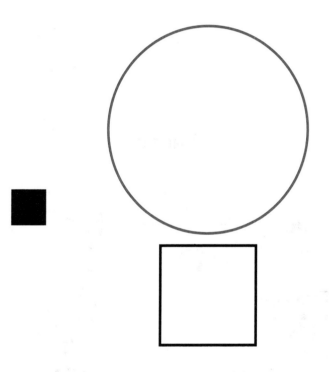

up and eat all my meals at regular hours.
She even took me to church. When I couldn't

the

MAGICIAN   BANJO
                              FLUTE

                      FARMER

        CORN

HAY STACK   GENIE
              BARN

"No, but I'm

"Who is the Wizard of Oz?" asked Dorothy.

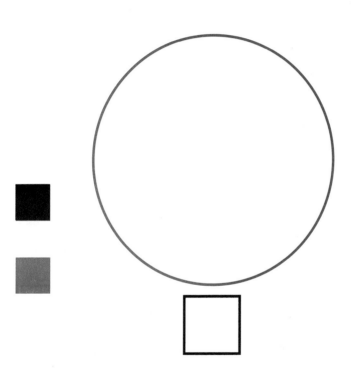

But it was rough living in a house all the time. The Widow made me wash and dress

waters of

very hot,"

"He is a great Wizard,"

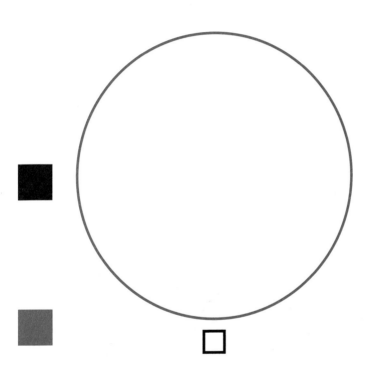

and raise me as her own son. She was kinda grateful, I guess, 'cause I helped save her life.

blue

TRACTOR   SILO

WHEAT
STALK

TRAILER

HORSE   WATER   MILK
SHOE   PUMP   CAN

the child

answered the Good Witch. "He is more

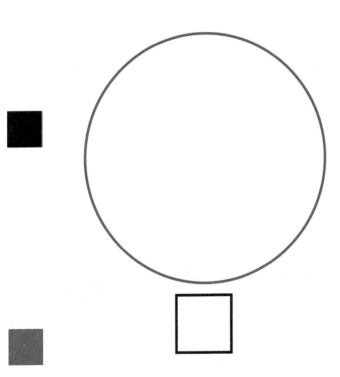

didn't make me happy. At about this time,
the Widow Douglas decided to take me in

sparkling

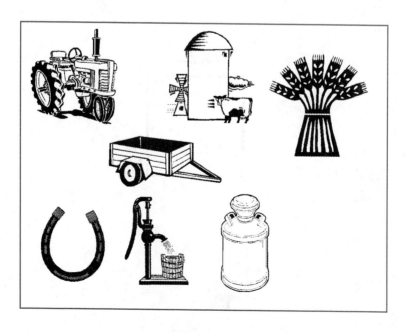

answered.

powerful than all of us put together.

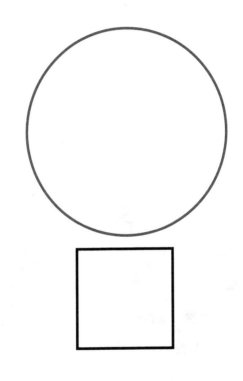

in that little town, it was more money than we knew what to do with. But the money

the

SHED

KEG

TROMBONE
PLAYER

BEER MUG

GINGERBREAD
MAN

SODA POP

"We'll be

He lives in the Emerald City.

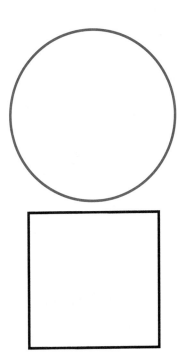

money in the bank for us, and we each got
an allowance of a dollar a day. For us,

bound for

there soon.

Only he can help you return to Kansas."

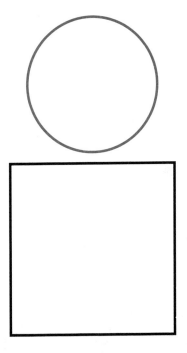

it was rightfully ours. Tom and I got six
thousand dollars apiece. The Judge put the

a ship

BREAD	PANCAKES	
STRAWBERRY	SALT AND PEPPER	SYRUP

Just keep

"How can I get to the Emerald City?"

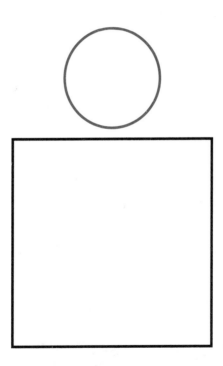

dollars in gold! It was money that had been
buried by robbers, so Judge Thatcher decided

boarded

going,

asked Dorothy. " You must walk,"

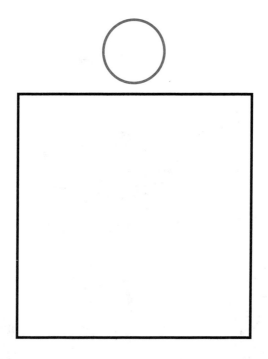

around here until Tom and I discovered a hidden treasure. We found twelve thousand

and

ICE CREAM SUNDAE	PIE
APPLE	PIZZA

and we'll

answered the Good Witch.

great adventures with my friend Tom
Sawyer. Things were always pretty dull

Switzerland

be there in

"You will see a Yellow Brick Road.

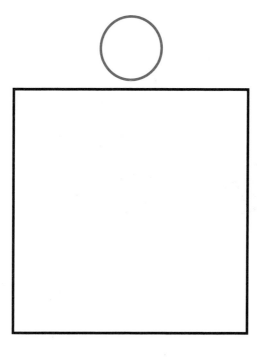

most of my life fishing on the banks of the
Mississippi, sleeping in doorways, and having

family left

CHERRIES

LEMONS

GRAPES

an hour. At

Follow that road and you will

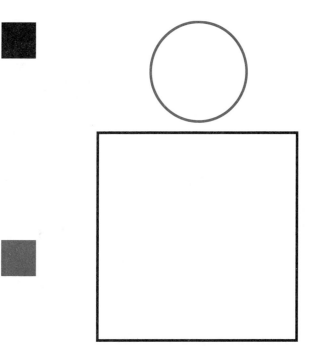

St. Petersburg, Missouri. My father is the town drunk and isn't around much. So I've spent

ago my

that

find the Wizard of Oz." Then the Good

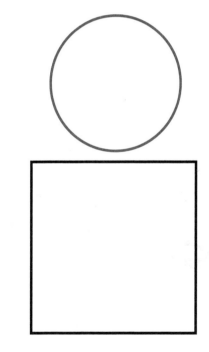

My name is Huckleberry Finn. I have
always lived in this same little town of

years

PEAR

COFFEE
CUP

moment a

Witch kissed Dorothy on

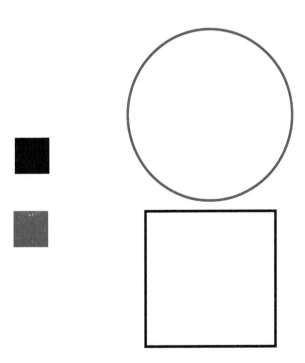

You might have heard of me if you read "The Adventures of Tom Sawyer" by Mark Twain.

Many

plump,

the forehead.

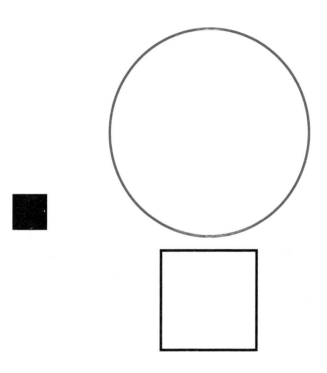